The
FOUR RULES
OF NUMBER
Fully Decimal and Metric

K. A. HESSE

LONGMAN

LONGMAN GROUP LIMITED
London

*Associated companies, branches and representatives
throughout the world*

First published 1956
Seventeenth impression 1974

Pupils' edition ISBN 0 582 18009 0
Teachers' edition ISBN 0 582 18010 4

Printed in Hong Kong by
Commonwealth Printing Press Ltd

CHECK YOUR ADDITION

Work across the page

A	1 +2	3 +0	2 +5	24 +63	42 +57
B	5 +16	3 +18	4 +26	48 +22	59 +38
C	11 12 13	11 10 26	12 21 17	26 30 7	35 4 45
D	22 13 15	43 20 54	25 10 75	20 34 46	58 7 82
E	32 13 47	25 46 80	23 56 88	89 86 25	69 98 4
F	47 26 57	58 73 69	374 105 268	338 80 572	658 99 876
G	123 243 115 425	65 373 400 197	273 647 89 675	463 97 84 406	413 69 907 86
H	386 576 989 78	342 153 265 104 376	1384 2678 1769 3007 2898	6768 4889 70 586 909	5785 8599 607 88 7895

Further Practice	
Table	Pages
1	2 & 3
2	4 & 5
2	6
2	7 to 9
3	10 & 11
4	12 to 14
5	15 & 16
6	17

ADDITION TABLE: 1
Work across the page

Add (+):

A	1+1=	1+0=	0+1=	0+0=	2+1=
B	1+2=	2+0=	0+2=	2+2=	3+0=
C	3+1=	1+3=	3+2=	0+3=	4+1=
D	2+3=	4+0=	5+1=	1+5=	5+0=
E	4+2=	1+4=	3+3=	6+1=	5+2=
F	2+4=	1+6=	0+6=	4+3=	3+4=
G	2+5=	1+7=	7+1=	8+1=	1+8=
H	5+3=	6+2=	4+4=	3+5=	2+6=
I	6+3=	5+4=	2+7=	7+2=	3+6=
J	3+4=	0+9=	4+5=	9+0=	2+7=

Add (+):

A	$\begin{array}{r}1\\+1\end{array}$	$\begin{array}{r}2\\+2\end{array}$	$\begin{array}{r}1\\+2\end{array}$	$\begin{array}{r}1\\+3\end{array}$	$\begin{array}{r}0\\+1\end{array}$	$\begin{array}{r}0\\+0\end{array}$	$\begin{array}{r}2\\+1\end{array}$	$\begin{array}{r}1\\+0\end{array}$
B	$\begin{array}{r}1\\+4\end{array}$	$\begin{array}{r}2\\+3\end{array}$	$\begin{array}{r}0\\+4\end{array}$	$\begin{array}{r}1\\+5\end{array}$	$\begin{array}{r}2\\+4\end{array}$	$\begin{array}{r}3\\+1\end{array}$	$\begin{array}{r}3\\+0\end{array}$	$\begin{array}{r}2\\+5\end{array}$
C	$\begin{array}{r}1\\+7\end{array}$	$\begin{array}{r}0\\+6\end{array}$	$\begin{array}{r}7\\+0\end{array}$	$\begin{array}{r}2\\+6\end{array}$	$\begin{array}{r}6\\+2\end{array}$	$\begin{array}{r}3\\+4\end{array}$	$\begin{array}{r}4\\+4\end{array}$	$\begin{array}{r}4\\+3\end{array}$
D	$\begin{array}{r}2\\+7\end{array}$	$\begin{array}{r}3\\+5\end{array}$	$\begin{array}{r}5\\+2\end{array}$	$\begin{array}{r}3\\+6\end{array}$	$\begin{array}{r}4\\+5\end{array}$	$\begin{array}{r}0\\+9\end{array}$	$\begin{array}{r}3\\+3\end{array}$	$\begin{array}{r}7\\+1\end{array}$

Add (+):   3

A   4   3   5   4   3   6   5
    +1   +2   +1   +2   +5   +3   +4

B   11   12   10   21   22   40   63
   +12   +11   +11   +13   +45   +38   +34

C   12   13   13   32   15   52   20
   +54   +75   +86   +33   +43   +23   +79

D   24   41   34   54   62   55   33
   +52   +58   +21   +14   +26   +43   +35

E   23   13   26   14   34   54   53
   +32   +64   +22   +63   +54   +43   +35

F   23   62   46   45   81   23   44
   +43   +15   +20   +32   +17   +65   +54

G   11   22   12   32   20   2   3
    21   23   21   30   12   32   20
    22   11   35   21   56   41   64

H   1   13   6   11   52   71   53
    53   34   20   22   14   17   15
    13   12   52   34   22   10   20

I   3   62   5   24   2   1   3
    21   12   40   14   74   85   64
    42   13   32   50   23   13   32

2⁰—F.R.N.

4

ADDITION TABLE: 2
Work across the page

Add (+):

A	9+1=	7+3=	1+9=	8+2=	2+8=
B	6+4=	4+6=	5+5=	3+7=	9+2=
C	9+3=	2+9=	7+4=	6+5=	4+7=
D	6+6=	9+3=	5+6=	8+3=	8+4=
E	3+8=	4+8=	7+5=	9+4=	8+5=
F	5+7=	3+9=	4+9=	7+6=	6+7=
G	9+5=	5+9=	5+8=	6+8=	8+6=
H	9+6=	6+9=	7+7=	8+7=	8+8=
I	7+8=	7+9=	8+9=	9+7=	9+9=

Add (+):

A	15 +14	16 +13	22 +17	2 +19	5 +16	6 +15	6 +16
B	3 +18	8 +13	4 +17	4 +18	4 +16	3 +17	6 +14
C	5 +15	6 +24	9 +22	3 +28	5 +17	7 +23	8 +23
D	7 +14	8 +12	6 +27	7 +25	1 +39	3 +49	5 +39
E	2 +19	5 +37	4 +28	3 +29	4 +39	5 +48	6 +47

Add (+):

A	11 +19	12 +18	18 +12	5 +15	9 +11	13 +17	5 +27
B	14 +26	17 +23	26 +14	24 +15	13 +36	6 +45	3 +57
C	29 +22	23 +18	34 +18	38 +13	49 +13	37 +24	26 +35
D	12 +49	13 +59	34 +27	46 +16	47 +27	15 +46	28 +48
E	25 +37	35 +18	46 +17	27 +35	38 +24	44 +19	34 +37
F	15 +49	29 +44	37 +36	36 +38	37 +48	36 +49	28 +57
G	27 +49	48 +25	39 +45	48 +36	38 +49	29 +56	37 +46
H	18 +58	58 +17	29 +57	59 +28	49 +39	48 +49	45 +49
I	12 12 37	13 12 26	12 21 38	24 13 26	22 23 16	21 14 35	13 25 24

6

Add (+):

A	12 22 15	11 10 28	10 34 17	12 13 15	11 12 27	23 22 15	14 30 16
B	15 12 14	15 10 34	25 20 35	3 26 31	3 17 41	7 42 12	6 30 34
C	6 43 33	15 4 14	14 6 42	20 6 57	6 10 74	50 8 28	40 5 44
D	12 20 29	8 10 23	9 30 12	9 21 33	7 30 26	4 10 49	6 55 10
E	5 20 28	16 13 5	18 30 5	28 14 30	17 30 7	19 2 33	25 30 7
F	17 30 28	19 24 20	28 26 30	15 9 40	29 5 30	8 20 47	5 35 40
G	18 37 21	26 29 30	19 6 50	29 50 7	37 9 30	28 4 43	36 34 20
H	24 33 20	16 34 4	27 7 51	35 40 9	28 50 7	47 35 4	39 47 12

Add (+):

A	22 +38	34 +56	21 +91	38 +91	40 +80	50 +66	70 +45
B	60 +45	86 +22	44 +60	74 +33	87 +32	93 +51	78 +61
C	91 +35	80 +40	13 +96	36 +70	50 +50	20 +80	60 +40
D	20 17 35	10 9 64	25 13 75	30 22 49	3 30 78	4 40 67	42 23 36
E	7 93 13	4 40 56	10 5 86	15 80 5	20 76 4	38 60 2	72 16 12
F	10 38 56	80 7 67	69 31 35	76 22 47	79 1 86	69 31 47	68 23 65
G	23 4 74	64 22 53	62 10 79	75 83 6	56 1 87	87 9 80	96 4 85
H	46 10 56	5 83 85	64 77 12	75 40 39	58 67 21	88 6 73	76 9 80

Write answers only

1	3+2.	**2**	3 plus 2.
3	4 plus 0.	**4**	7 plus 4.
5	6 plus 7.	**6**	8 plus 3.
7	Add 4 to 6.	**8**	Add 5 to 7.
9	Add 9 to 3.	**10**	Add 4 to 8.
11	Add five to four.	**12**	Add three to six.
13	To 6 add 5.	**14**	To 7 add 7.
15	Total 7 and 3.	**16**	Total 2 and 9.
17	Total 3 and 8.	**18**	Total 8 and 5.
19	Total 3, 4 and 2.	**20**	Total 5, 3 and 2
21	Six plus six.	**22**	Nine plus four.
23	Seven plus six.	**24**	Five plus nine.
25	Add five to eight.	**26**	Add seven to eight.
27	Add eight and eight.	**28**	To seven add nine.
29	Total nine and eight.	**30**	Total nine and nine.
31	Total six, three and five.	**32**	Total five, three and six.
33	Total one, four and nine.	**34**	Total six, three and nine.

1   To 23 add 45.

2   Add 27 and 62.

3   What is 36 plus 42?

4   What is 35 plus 44?

5   Find the total of twenty and forty-six.

6   Find the total of twenty and fifty-four.

7   What is the total of fifty-one and sixty-nine?

8   What is the total of forty-eight and seventy-two?

9   What is thirty-seven plus eighty-eight?

10   What is twenty-six plus eighty-nine?

11   Find the total of thirty, twenty-one and forty-nine.

12   What is the total of 17, 40 and 36?

13   What is the total of nineteen, thirty and fifty-seven?

14   What is the total of eighteen, forty and forty-nine?

15   Find the total of twenty-five, forty and thirty-six.

16   Find the total of twenty-six, thirty-seven and forty-two.

17   What is seventy-one plus eighty-nine?

18   What is eighty-nine plus eighty-one?

19   Is sixty-five plus fifty-six greater than one hundred and forty?

20   Is seventy-four plus forty-seven greater than one hundred and fifty?

21   At darts Tom scored nineteen, eleven and sixty. What was the total?

22   Tom has 38 red marbles 40 blue and forty-seven green ones. What is the total?

ADDITION TABLE: 3
Work across the page

Add (+):

A	10+1=	10+0=	11+1=	10+2=	12+1=
B	11+2=	10+3=	10+4=	13+1=	14+1=
C	11+3=	12+2=	12+3=	15+1=	16+1=
D	15+0=	10+5=	11+5=	10+6=	17+1=
E	11+4=	12+4=	14+0=	11+6=	10+7=
F	11+7=	12+5=	13+2=	13+3=	10+8=
G	11+8=	18+1=	12+6=	14+2=	15+2=
H	12+7=	12+8=	10+9=	11+9=	12+9=
I	13+4=	14+4=	14+3=	13+5=	15+3=

Add (+):

A	11 11 29	12 24 17	21 15 46	11 34 26	22 13 37	23 25 35	4 40 46

B	11 33 18	22 16 26	23 34 8	13 22 9	24 6 44	35 9 41	26 57 3

C	23 42 54	23 60 46	44 24 91	53 30 85	30 93 24	25 42 80	64 40 75

D	33 54 44	61 55 37	21 67 49	14 43 87	22 75 78	31 68 69	23 56 88

Add (+):

A	41	53	24	63	16	12	42
	10	29	75	40	40	70	70
	93	80	52	77	90	87	48

B	54	12	13	41	47	46	85
	45	71	76	50	50	67	80
	70	86	93	98	75	60	16

C	79	59	38	37	28	14	58
	52	69	72	54	58	93	7
	58	51	79	68	99	89	63

D	65	45	61	73	39	4	59
	4	54	35	5	68	87	48
	88	9	9	28	82	17	4

E	26	18	58	49	49	12	33
	76	68	39	98	47	88	9
	6	34	3	3	4	57	65

F	35	81	43	84	19	89	97
	74	59	86	96	80	77	56
	69	60	49	28	79	35	56

G	88	8	79	99	67	49	92
	78	99	52	68	55	43	98
	24	93	39	33	56	59	26

H	64	81	39	99	84	98	99
	6	97	8	20	6	9	23
	95	19	84	99	98	93	89

ADDITION TABLE: 4
Work across the page

Add (+):

A	13+7 =	17+2 =	16+2 =	18+2 =	16+3 =
B	15+4 =	14+5 =	13+8 =	18+3 =	14+6 =
C	17+3 =	16+4 =	13+9 =	15+5 =	15+6 =
D	14+7 =	17+4 =	18+4 =	14+8 =	14+9 =
E	15+7 =	17+5 =	15+8 =	18+5 =	16+5 =
F	16+6 =	17+6 =	16+7 =	18+6 =	16+8 =
G	17+0 =	15+9 =	16+9 =	17+7 =	17+8 =
H	18+7 =	17+9 =	18+8 =	18+9 =	17+9 =

Add (+):

A	27 15 37	7 56 47	54 77 69	42 68 98	8 42 99	35 86 98	28 97 56
B	52 69 79	26 76 79	46 65 79	23 78 89	53 48 98	54 54 99	37 78 76
C	44 48 79	46 54 89	37 56 97	58 75 78	69 86 67	58 85 79	45 79 85
D	43 99 49	35 99 67	57 98 55	46 89 74	89 95 38	47 79 96	66 78 59

Add (+):

A	46	57	127	204	26	313	112
	96	88	136	107	209	45	407
	79	89	219	388	359	539	179

B	207	394	269	224	143	184	45
	156	105	386	168	137	167	256
	358	278	187	478	599	367	698

C	174	267	447	145	279	69	423
	453	355	375	584	132	444	98
	59	78	69	78	488	378	279

D	352	474	535	296	238	452	23
	69	69	77	120	80	69	388
	389	358	188	384	582	379	289

E	476	698	255	487	289	387	279
	66	53	87	98	86	398	598
	58	49	379	148	349	69	78

F	589	293	99	699	784	66	118
	99	67	554	76	60	497	90
	78	339	68	58	56	58	702

G	89	71	98	79	463	378	597
	540	684	340	588	499	266	368
	504	404	706	560	369	489	479

H	580	368	579	698	854	479	658
	176	477	98	639	979	908	99
	68	199	378	708	799	679	876

ADDITION WITH WORDS (3)

Write answers only

1 Nine plus five.

2 The total of 6 and 7.

3 The sum of 8 and 5.

4 Increase 5 by 3.

5 Increase 9 by 7.

6 The total of 8 and 6.

7 Increase 10 by 3.

8 The sum of 10 and 7.

9 Increase 14 by 6.

10 Increase 13 by 7.

11 Fifteen plus eight.

12 Sixteen plus five.

13 Fifteen plus nine.

14 The sum of 17 plus six.

15 Increase 18 by 9.

16 Add 8 plus 6 plus 7.

Work out on paper

17 What is the total of forty-four and seventy?

18 Find the sum of 67 and 76.

19 Increase thirty-six by eighty-four.

20 What is four-hundred-and-seven increased by sixty-nine?

21 Find the total of ninety-eight, seventy-six and fifty-eight.

22 Increase three-hundred-and-eight by ninety-seven.

23 What is the sum of twenty-three, forty and seventy-seven?

24 Find the total of ninety-three, seven and thirty-nine.

25 What is the total when 467 is increased by 59?

26 Add fifty-seven to the sum of two-hundred-and-sixty-three and four-hundred-and-eight.

ADDITION TABLE: 5

Work across the page

Add (+):

A	19+1=	19+0=	20+1=	19+2=	21+1=
B	20+2=	19+3=	22+1=	21+2=	20+3=
C	19+4=	23+1=	23+3=	21+3=	20+4=
D	19+5=	21+4=	22+2=	22+3=	20+5=
E	22+4=	19+6=	20+6=	21+5=	24+1=
F	23+2=	19+7=	19+8=	20+7=	21+6=
G	24+0=	24+2=	25+0=	25+1=	24+3=
H	23+4=	19+9=	20+8=	20+9=	22+5=
I	19+0=	21+7=	21+8=	22+6=	22+7=

Add (+):

A	176	768	956	248	598	364	246
	588	886	698	907	69	900	75
	358	679	800	399	788	805	909

B	124	231	400	352	435	265	354
	233	106	251	375	464	373	478
	115	412	130	284	943	97	807
	625	504	219	308	375	508	693

C	202	342	465	375	489	378	508
	734	685	256	136	705	687	399
	686	759	887	908	389	450	776
	855	486	549	697	990	879	588

D	397	279	58	419	231	212	373
	405	686	30	283	395	745	547
	284	53	909	56	786	376	89
	608	238	409	248	409	888	675

16

Add (+):

A	2 1 2	1 1 9	3 1 3	5 1 1	7 3 4	4 1 3
	5 6 7	4 0 0	6 9 4	4 3	4 8 0	2 5 6
	6 5 8	5 8 9	5 0 7	3 4 9	5 7 8	8 7 9
	8 9 6	7 7 9	8 9 9	9 7	2 0 8	7 9 7

B	4 6 5	1 4 5	2 6 1	4 2	3 2 9	5 3 2
	6 4 3	6 4 6	6 0 5	7 9 5	5 0 0	6 7 8
	5 7 8	4 7 7	6 9 7	6 8	7 9 9	6 9 7
	7 6 8	8 9 7	9 9 9	9 5 6	5 8 9	7 5 9

C	1 7 7	6 3	5 5 8	1 0 4 0	1 7 6 4	2 6 5 3
	3 2 4	6 9 7	4 1	2 6 0 7	2 0 5 5	1 0 9 7
	5 7 7	4 8	8 9	1 0 9 8	2 9 7 9	3 8 0 4
	9 8 9	7 6 9	6 8 9	3 8 9 9	1 8 8 9	1 0 7 8

D	1 8 9 8	1 4 2 1	2 3 2 4	1 5 3 6	3 1 1 4	5 2 3 2
	2 9 0 5	2 3 0 8	1 6 4 3	3 0 5 3	6 5 9	6 9 8
	2 5 8 7	1 8 9 7	4 7 8 8	9 6 8	3 8 7 5	9 0 7 5
	1 5 9 8	3 6 9 9	1 5 7 9	2 9 8 8	4 7 8 7	8 5 6

ADDITION TABLE: 6

Work across the page

Add (+):

A	3+5=	13+5=	23+5=	20+9=	25+2=
B	2+8=	12+8=	22+8=	26+1=	25+3=
C	3+7=	13+7=	23+7=	26+2=	27+3=
D	8+3=	18+3=	28+3=	24+4=	21+9=
E	4+7=	14+7=	24+7=	23+8=	27+1=
F	25+4=	24+5=	27+2=	26+3=	22+9=
G	25+5=	24+7=	27+4=	26+5=	25+6=
H	25+7=	26+6=	27+6=	24+8=	23+9=
I	26+7=	25+8=	27+7=	24+9=	26+8=

Add (+):

A

115	241	596	768	587	476
476	357	378	307	96	586
388	488	456	97	778	979
689	599	769	858	689	78

B

895	546	69	568	797	683
68	99	560	89	99	79
989	377	898	697	659	88
307	579	678	806	608	969

C

1796	1465	786	5786	6785	7436
1984	3989	5496	798	799	798
2509	2796	5779	6969	5948	867
3879	5708	6908	5258	7478	5989

D

153	2875	6874	4756	6497	7586
342	384	4596	5697	678	4899
265	6459	9087	769	986	60
206	696	959	884	7569	589
374	9508	968	6079	8005	809

E

3564	635	5946	5785	4567	6987
8360	7075	889	4668	8599	98
876	8964	5793	8697	9698	809
9758	689	927	849	6706	70
4096	6587	4698	1076	7859	956

F

5463	7809	657	498	3078	6789
87	697	6978	4069	879	5008
8000	9	69	97	90	87
99	698	697	786	908	9
688	87	85	9	8070	878

CHECK YOUR
SUBTRACTION

		Further Practice	
		Table	Pages

A

3	4	5	7	9
−2	−0	−3	−4	−5

Table	Pages
1	19

B

85	76	80	37	89
−32	−50	−50	−33	−87

Table	Pages
1	20

C

10	20	70	51	92
− 7	− 9	−13	−14	−25

Table	Pages
2	21 & 22

D

40	367	450	530	862
−38	−162	−200	−315	−157

Table	Pages
2	23

E

416	505	623	800	721
−296	−210	−583	−206	− 66

Table	Pages
2	24 to 26

F

503	450	664	500	876
−346	− 67	−196	−292	−797

Table	Pages
3	27 & 28

G

6005	7090	32786	58991	80990
−5096	− 999	−20690	− 1093	−79997

Table	Pages
3	30

SUBTRACTION TABLE: 1
Work across the page

Take away (−):

A	$2-1=$	$1-0=$	$0-0=$	$1-1=$	$2-0=$
B	$2-2=$	$3-1=$	$3-0=$	$3-2=$	$3-3=$
C	$4-1=$	$4-3=$	$4-4=$	$4-0=$	$4-2=$
D	$5-1=$	$5-4=$	$5-5=$	$6-6=$	$6-0=$
E	$5-0=$	$6-1=$	$6-5=$	$7-0=$	$7-7=$
F	$7-1=$	$7-6=$	$8-8=$	$8-0=$	$8-1=$
G	$8-7=$	$9-0=$	$9-9=$	$9-1=$	$9-8=$

Take away (−):

A	$\begin{array}{r}2\\-1\end{array}$	$\begin{array}{r}1\\-1\end{array}$	$\begin{array}{r}0\\-0\end{array}$	$\begin{array}{r}2\\-2\end{array}$	$\begin{array}{r}4\\-4\end{array}$	$\begin{array}{r}1\\-0\end{array}$	$\begin{array}{r}2\\-0\end{array}$	$\begin{array}{r}3\\-3\end{array}$
B	$\begin{array}{r}3\\-1\end{array}$	$\begin{array}{r}3\\-0\end{array}$	$\begin{array}{r}4\\-1\end{array}$	$\begin{array}{r}4\\-3\end{array}$	$\begin{array}{r}4\\-2\end{array}$	$\begin{array}{r}4\\-0\end{array}$	$\begin{array}{r}4\\-4\end{array}$	$\begin{array}{r}3\\-2\end{array}$
C	$\begin{array}{r}4\\-3\end{array}$	$\begin{array}{r}3\\-2\end{array}$	$\begin{array}{r}3\\-1\end{array}$	$\begin{array}{r}4\\-1\end{array}$	$\begin{array}{r}4\\-2\end{array}$	$\begin{array}{r}2\\1\end{array}$	$\begin{array}{r}2\\-2\end{array}$	$\begin{array}{r}4\\-0\end{array}$
D	$\begin{array}{r}4\\-4\end{array}$	$\begin{array}{r}5\\-5\end{array}$	$\begin{array}{r}5\\-0\end{array}$	$\begin{array}{r}5\\-1\end{array}$	$\begin{array}{r}5\\-4\end{array}$	$\begin{array}{r}6\\-6\end{array}$	$\begin{array}{r}6\\-1\end{array}$	$\begin{array}{r}6\\-5\end{array}$
E	$\begin{array}{r}5\\-0\end{array}$	$\begin{array}{r}5\\-1\end{array}$	$\begin{array}{r}5\\-4\end{array}$	$\begin{array}{r}5\\-5\end{array}$	$\begin{array}{r}6\\-0\end{array}$	$\begin{array}{r}6\\-6\end{array}$	$\begin{array}{r}7\\-7\end{array}$	$\begin{array}{r}8\\-8\end{array}$
F	$\begin{array}{r}7\\-0\end{array}$	$\begin{array}{r}8\\-0\end{array}$	$\begin{array}{r}9\\-0\end{array}$	$\begin{array}{r}7\\-1\end{array}$	$\begin{array}{r}7\\-6\end{array}$	$\begin{array}{r}8\\-7\end{array}$	$\begin{array}{r}8\\-1\end{array}$	$\begin{array}{r}9\\-1\end{array}$

20 Take away (—):

A	6 −6	6 −0	6 −5	7 −6	8 −7	9 −1	9 −8
B	3 2 −2 1	2 3 −1 2	3 3 −1 0	4 2 −3 0	5 4 −1 1	4 5 −2 0	6 6 −1 0
C	7 5 −1 4	7 7 −6 0	7 4 −1 2	5 8 −4 0	6 5 −5 1	4 6 −3 5	8 7 −1 0
D	6 5 −1 0	4 4 −3 1	7 7 −6 1	8 9 −7 0	8 8 −1 0	9 9 −8 1	7 9 −6 8
E	3 9 −1 0	3 2 −2 2	6 3 −1 3	5 5 −4 5	5 4 −1 4	6 6 −1 6	8 5 −1 5
F	6 1 −5 1	4 6 −2 6	9 7 −1 7	9 8 −8 8	8 0 −7 0	7 9 −1 0	8 9 −7 9
G	4 3 −1 3	8 8 −1 8	2 4 −1 4	7 0 −0 0	5 9 −1 9	5 8 −4 8	9 0 −1 0
H	6 6 −5 6	2 3 −2 1	3 5 −3 4	4 4 −4 0	8 3 −8 0	5 2 −5 0	9 7 −9 6
I	7 7 −7 1	7 7 −7 6	8 8 −8 7	6 8 −6 1	7 9 −7 1	8 9 −8 8	9 9 −9 8

SUBTRACTION TABLE: 2

Work across the page

Take away (—):

A	$5-2=$	$5-3=$	$6-2=$	$6-4=$	$6-3=$
B	$7-5=$	$7-2=$	$7-3=$	$7-4=$	$8-2=$
C	$9-2=$	$9-7=$	$8-6=$	$8-3=$	$8-5=$
D	$8-4=$	$9-6=$	$9-3=$	$9-5=$	$9-4=$
E	$10-9=$	$10-1=$	$10-8=$	$11-9=$	$10-2=$
F	$11-2=$	$11-3=$	$10-3=$	$10-7=$	$11-7=$
G	$10-6=$	$10-4=$	$11-4=$	$11-6=$	$10-5=$
H	$11-5=$	$11-8=$	$12-3=$	$12-9=$	$12-6—$

Take away (—):

A	$\begin{array}{r}59\\-30\\\hline\end{array}$	$\begin{array}{r}58\\-20\\\hline\end{array}$	$\begin{array}{r}76\\-32\\\hline\end{array}$	$\begin{array}{r}65\\-32\\\hline\end{array}$	$\begin{array}{r}78\\-23\\\hline\end{array}$	$\begin{array}{r}60\\-40\\\hline\end{array}$	$\begin{array}{r}95\\-75\\\hline\end{array}$
B	$\begin{array}{r}10\\-1\\\hline\end{array}$	$\begin{array}{r}10\\-9\\\hline\end{array}$	$\begin{array}{r}10\\-2\\\hline\end{array}$	$\begin{array}{r}10\\-3\\\hline\end{array}$	$\begin{array}{r}10\\-7\\\hline\end{array}$	$\begin{array}{r}10\\-8\\\hline\end{array}$	$\begin{array}{r}10\\-5\\\hline\end{array}$
C	$\begin{array}{r}10\\-4\\\hline\end{array}$	$\begin{array}{r}10\\-6\\\hline\end{array}$	$\begin{array}{r}10\\-3\\\hline\end{array}$	$\begin{array}{r}10\\-2\\\hline\end{array}$	$\begin{array}{r}10\\-8\\\hline\end{array}$	$\begin{array}{r}10\\-7\\\hline\end{array}$	$\begin{array}{r}10\\-5\\\hline\end{array}$
D	$\begin{array}{r}10\\-6\\\hline\end{array}$	$\begin{array}{r}20\\-6\\\hline\end{array}$	$\begin{array}{r}20\\-1\\\hline\end{array}$	$\begin{array}{r}20\\-9\\\hline\end{array}$	$\begin{array}{r}20\\-5\\\hline\end{array}$	$\begin{array}{r}30\\-3\\\hline\end{array}$	$\begin{array}{r}30\\-4\\\hline\end{array}$
E	$\begin{array}{r}20\\-1\\\hline\end{array}$	$\begin{array}{r}30\\-2\\\hline\end{array}$	$\begin{array}{r}40\\-5\\\hline\end{array}$	$\begin{array}{r}40\\-6\\\hline\end{array}$	$\begin{array}{r}50\\-7\\\hline\end{array}$	$\begin{array}{r}70\\-9\\\hline\end{array}$	$\begin{array}{r}80\\-8\\\hline\end{array}$
F	$\begin{array}{r}10\\-9\\\hline\end{array}$	$\begin{array}{r}40\\-4\\\hline\end{array}$	$\begin{array}{r}50\\-8\\\hline\end{array}$	$\begin{array}{r}60\\-6\\\hline\end{array}$	$\begin{array}{r}60\\-3\\\hline\end{array}$	$\begin{array}{r}80\\-5\\\hline\end{array}$	$\begin{array}{r}90\\-7\\\hline\end{array}$

Take away (—):

A

10	20	30	50	70	90	90
− 2	− 1	− 0	− 0	− 8	− 6	− 7

B

60	30	40	60	50	80	90
− 3	−19	−19	−19	−19	−19	−19

C

70	30	50	50	60	70	80
−19	−11	−18	−12	−18	−13	−17

D

80	90	40	40	40	50	50
−14	−15	−29	−21	−25	−25	−29

E

60	60	70	80	70	90	80
−29	−32	−34	−42	−43	−26	−35

F

31	31	41	71	32	52	42
−19	−12	−12	−22	−19	−39	−23

G

51	52	71	62	81	82	92
−29	−36	−33	−29	−58	−43	−56

H

71	61	91	92	81	72	91
−44	−15	−37	−46	−66	−59	−68

I

80	81	72	91	82	92	92
−11	−17	−46	−15	−53	−36	−59

Take away (−):

A

80	71	81	90	91	82	92
−15	−13	−46	−28	−47	−33	−66

B

30	50	60	40	51	31	62
−23	−47	−55	−36	−45	−23	−53

C

41	61	52	70	81	90	92
−34	−53	−46	−64	−76	−82	−89

D

550	340	406	507	610	830	704
−230	−120	−205	−103	−200	−500	−200

E

615	706	836	488	609	770	899
−210	−306	−306	−180	−402	−450	−353

F

801	673	690	708	890	898	909
−401	−373	−400	−206	−290	−668	−704

G

989	450	650	861	781	781	871
−239	−129	−431	−339	−347	−456	−458

H

391	932	741	621	752	971	891
−149	−323	−534	−315	−543	−763	−262

I

460	520	942	760	832	981	990
−113	−207	−633	−302	−209	−324	−427

Take away (−):

A	406 −192	310 −190	511 −181	710 −120	524 −233	613 −243	917 −353
B	841 −637	819 −146	809 −222	906 −236	817 −354	729 −494	808 −442
C	809 −655	319 −266	418 −375	503 −453	226 −195	518 −423	707 −694
D	410 −130	310 −230	212 −142	604 −564	417 −357	809 −779	728 −668
E	511 −461	340 −108	331 −207	461 −308	682 −603	700 −610	871 −802
F	400 −181	500 −271	401 −214	612 −386	502 −306	600 −204	701 −305
G	600 −309	410 − 53	602 − 49	511 − 77	701 − 58	800 − 17	912 − 83
H	700 −207	512 − 13	811 − 14	607 −527	111 − 43	101 − 26	802 −739
I	702 −306	601 −105	600 −580	812 −779	702 − 89	822 −703	900 −801

Write answers only

1 From 7 take 3.		**2** From 7 take 4.
3 From 9 take 1.		**4** Take 0 from 9.
5 Take 3 from 8.		**6** Take 6 from 8.
7 From 9 take 2.		**8** Take 5 from 9.
9 Take 3 from 10.		**10** From 9 take 6.
11 Take 7 from 10.		**12** From 10 take 2.
13 From 10 take 6.		**14** Take 4 from 10.
15 Subtract 5 from 8.		**16** Subtract 2 from 7.
17 Subtract 4 from 9.		**18** Subtract 7 from 9.
19 Take 2 from 11.		**20** From 9 take 3.
21 Subtract 3 from 11.		**22** Subtract 4 from 11.
23 From 11 take 5.		**24** Take 3 from 12.
25 Subtract 6 from 11.		**26** From 11 take 7.
27 Take 8 from 10.		**28** Subtract 7 from 10.
29 From 11 take 8.		**30** Take 6 from 12.
31 Subtract 9 from 10.		**32** Subtract 8 from 11.
33 8 minus 4.		**34** 10 minus 3.
35 9 minus 9.		**36** 11 minus 11.
37 11 minus 9.		**38** 11 minus 0.
39 Subtract 9 from 12.		**40** 12 minus 9.

Work out on paper

1 From 88 take 35.

2 From 77 take 43.

3 Take 26 from 96.

4 Take 34 from 94.

5 Subtract thirty-one from seventy.

6 Subtract forty-nine from eighty.

7 Sixty-two minus thirty-three.

8 Ninety-one minus fifty-six.

9 By how many is ninety greater than fifty-one?

10 By how many is 372 greater than 129?

11 By how many is 450 greater than 208?

12 By how many is 690 greater than 306?

13 Subtract one hundred and twenty from three hundred.

14 Subtract one hundred and thirty from four hundred.

15 How much less than 91 is 25?

16 How many less than 309 is 155?

17 How many less than 318 is 175?

18 Five hundred and ten minus seventy.

19 By how many is 146 less than 526?

20 By how many is 394 less than 629?

21 By how many is five hundred and eighty-two greater than five hundred and three?

22 By how many is eight hundred and six less than eight hundred and eighty?

SUBTRACTION TABLE: 3

Work across the page

Take away (—):

A 12−10=	12− 4=	13− 4=	13− 9=	14− 5=
B 12− 5=	13− 5=	12− 7=	13− 6=	13− 7=
C 12− 8=	13− 8=	14− 6= .	14− 8=	14− 7=
D 15− 6=	15− 9=	14− 9=	15− 7=	15− 8=
E 16− 7=	17− 8=	10−10=	11−10=	13−10=
F 16− 8=	16−10=	14−10=	15−10=	16− 9=
G 17− 9=	18−10=	17−10=	19−10=	18− 9=

Take away (—):

A

322	420	243	352	463	342	456
−115	−240	−144	−157	−265	−258	−368

B

524	637	505	705	243	435	547
−236	−548	−377	−248	− 67	− 79	− 79

C

470	743	568	602	503	334	754
−373	−689	− 89	−505	−134	−255	−656

D

502	443	526	343	456	630	840
−257	− 67	− 77	−278	−378	− 87	−785

E

465	787	312	423	532	643	754
−189	−689	−184	−134	−235	−245	−286

F

543	664	475	382	793	574	882
−166	−365	−286	−187	−387	−367	−488
377	299	189	195	406	207	394

28

Take away (—):

A

413	324	433	745	654	566
−298	−198	−299	−498	−399	−298
175	126	134	247	255	278

B

595	637	412	523	233	444
−197	−498	−195	−294	− 95	− 95
398	139	217	229	138	349

C

452	372	763	482	672	793
−297	− 98	− 96	− 97	− 98	− 97
155	274	667	385	574	

D

613	710	890	697	510	600
−399	−495	−299	−394	−299	−391
274	215	591	303	211	209

E

500	400	600	500	800	800
−299	−193	−494	−196	−498	−297
201	207	106	304	302	803

F

733	243	125	144	254	165
−395	− 96	− 96	− 99	−197	− 97
338	147	29	45	57	68

G

870	603	494	686	796	560
− 98	− 98	−398	−599	−397	−409
772	505				

H

400	500	300	600	503	700
−309	−205	− 91	− 97	−107	− 93

I

205	734	190	596	706	845
−106	−697	− 99	−497	−698	−798

Write answers only:

1 13 minus 6.

2 15 minus 7.

3 Reduce 13 by 5.

4 Reduce 15 by 8.

5 Reduce 17 by 10.

6 Reduce 14 by 9.

7 Subtract 8 from 16.

8 18 minus 10.

9 Find the difference between 12 and 8.

10 Find the difference between 15 and 7.

11 Find the difference between 9 and 16.

12 By how much is 19 greater than 10?

Work out on paper:

13 Reduce eighty-three by forty-seven.

14 Subtract four-hundred-and-twenty from six-hundred.

15 By how much is six-hundred-and-six less than eight-hundred?

16 Find the difference between 307 and 401

17 Find the difference between seven-hundred-and-one and ninety-nine.

18 Reduce eight-hundred by five-hundred-and-ninety-nine.

19 Find the difference between 703 and 900.

20 Reduce 7001 by 6009.

Take away (—):

A	394 −196	605 −297	503 −198	404 − 98	695 − 98
B	6476 −3278	4527 −1898	3055 −1299	4706 −1809	3767 −1999
C	5602 − 804	4384 − 395	6512 − 505	4432 −3997	5508 − 909
D	3393 − 595	3604 −2976	5003 − 957	7542 −6668	1043 − 978
E	1356 − 977	7000 − 991	5076 −1078	6043 − 989	8008 −7009
F	1005 − 909	2006 −1099	4007 −3909	8000 −7995	1870 − 999
G	4132 −2944	35003 −24574	52324 −18545	62254 −19656	
H	34303 −16907	74900 −29991	60105 −50097	84151 −74154	
I	66566 − 9968	18765 − 9989	10087 − 9089	90003 −80906	

CHECK YOUR MULTIPLICATION

					Further Practice	
					Table	**Pages**
A	$\begin{array}{r} 12 \\ \times\ 2 \\ \hline \end{array}$	$\begin{array}{r} 31 \\ \times\ 3 \\ \hline \end{array}$	$\begin{array}{r} 40 \\ \times\ 5 \\ \hline \end{array}$	$\begin{array}{r} 62 \\ \times\ 4 \\ \hline \end{array}$	1	32
B	$\begin{array}{r} 14 \\ \times\ 3 \\ \hline \end{array}$	$\begin{array}{r} 25 \\ \times\ 4 \\ \hline \end{array}$	$\begin{array}{r} 54 \\ \times\ 5 \\ \hline \end{array}$	$\begin{array}{r} 65 \\ \times\ 6 \\ \hline \end{array}$	1	33 & 34
C	$\begin{array}{r} 28 \\ \times\ 2 \\ \hline \end{array}$	$\begin{array}{r} 67 \\ \times\ 3 \\ \hline \end{array}$	$\begin{array}{r} 89 \\ \times\ 6 \\ \hline \end{array}$	$\begin{array}{r} 97 \\ \times\ 9 \\ \hline \end{array}$	2	36 & 37
D	$\begin{array}{r} 420 \\ \times\ 3 \\ \hline \end{array}$	$\begin{array}{r} 215 \\ \times\ 4 \\ \hline \end{array}$	$\begin{array}{r} 240 \\ \times\ 5 \\ \hline \end{array}$	$\begin{array}{r} 605 \\ \times\ 6 \\ \hline \end{array}$	2	38
E	$\begin{array}{r} 306 \\ \times\ 5 \\ \hline \end{array}$	$\begin{array}{r} 879 \\ \times\ 4 \\ \hline \end{array}$	$\begin{array}{r} 709 \\ \times\ 7 \\ \hline \end{array}$	$\begin{array}{r} 897 \\ \times\ 9 \\ \hline \end{array}$	2	39
F	$\begin{array}{r} 43 \\ \times\ 10 \\ \hline \end{array}$	$\begin{array}{r} 156 \\ \times\ 11 \\ \hline \end{array}$	$\begin{array}{r} 505 \\ \times\ 12 \\ \hline \end{array}$	$\begin{array}{r} 678 \\ \times\ 12 \\ \hline \end{array}$	3	41 & 42
G	$\begin{array}{r} 491 \\ \times\ 11 \\ \hline \end{array}$	$\begin{array}{r} 699 \\ \times\ 11 \\ \hline \end{array}$	$\begin{array}{r} 509 \\ \times\ 12 \\ \hline \end{array}$	$\begin{array}{r} 789 \\ \times\ 12 \\ \hline \end{array}$	3	42G

PREPARING FOR MULTIPLICATION
Work across the page

Extending addition (+):

A	$20+1=$	$20+2=$	$24+1=$	$20+3=$	$24+2=$
B	$25+1=$	$25+2=$	$24+3=$	$25+3=$	$30+1=$
C	$30+2=$	$36+1=$	$36+2=$	$30+3=$	$36+3=$

MULTIPLICATION TABLE: 1

Multiply (✗):

D	$2\times1=$	$2\times0=$	$2\times2=$	$3\times1=$	$3\times0=$
E	$4\times1=$	$1\times4=$	$0\times4=$	$2\times3=$	$3\times2=$
F	$5\times0=$	$2\times4=$	$4\times2=$	$3\times3=$	$2\times5=$
G	$3\times4=$	$4\times3=$	$3\times5=$	$4\times4=$	$5\times3=$
H	$5\times2=$	$6\times1=$	$2\times6=$	$6\times2=$	$4\times5=$
I	$0\times6=$	$5\times4=$	$6\times4=$	$4\times6=$	$6\times3=$
J	$3\times6=$	$5\times5=$	$6\times5=$	$5\times6=$	$6\times6=$

Multiply (✗):

A	$\begin{array}{r}12\\ \times\ 2\\ \hline\end{array}$	$\begin{array}{r}13\\ \times\ 2\\ \hline\end{array}$	$\begin{array}{r}12\\ \times\ 3\\ \hline\end{array}$	$\begin{array}{r}11\\ \times\ 4\\ \hline\end{array}$	$\begin{array}{r}14\\ \times\ 2\\ \hline\end{array}$	$\begin{array}{r}12\\ \times\ 4\\ \hline\end{array}$
B	$\begin{array}{r}13\\ \times\ 3\\ \hline\end{array}$	$\begin{array}{r}10\\ \times\ 2\\ \hline\end{array}$	$\begin{array}{r}10\\ \times\ 3\\ \hline\end{array}$	$\begin{array}{r}20\\ \times\ 2\\ \hline\end{array}$	$\begin{array}{r}30\\ \times\ 2\\ \hline\end{array}$	$\begin{array}{r}20\\ \times\ 4\\ \hline\end{array}$
C	$\begin{array}{r}20\\ \times\ 3\\ \hline\end{array}$	$\begin{array}{r}21\\ \times\ 4\\ \hline\end{array}$	$\begin{array}{r}40\\ \times\ 2\\ \hline\end{array}$	$\begin{array}{r}44\\ \times\ 2\\ \hline\end{array}$	$\begin{array}{r}30\\ \times\ 3\\ \hline\end{array}$	$\begin{array}{r}41\\ \times\ 4\\ \hline\end{array}$
D	$\begin{array}{r}10\\ \times\ 5\\ \hline\end{array}$	$\begin{array}{r}30\\ \times\ 4\\ \hline\end{array}$	$\begin{array}{r}30\\ \times\ 5\\ \hline\end{array}$	$\begin{array}{r}61\\ \times\ 3\\ \hline\end{array}$	$\begin{array}{r}31\\ \times\ 5\\ \hline\end{array}$	$\begin{array}{r}40\\ \times\ 4\\ \hline\end{array}$

A	31 × 4	60 × 2	32 × 3	51 × 2	50 × 3	42 × 4

B	32 × 4	30 × 4	40 × 5	50 × 4	54 × 2	51 × 3

C	41 × 5	43 × 3	53 × 3	62 × 3	60 × 4	63 × 3

D	51 × 4	52 × 4	62 × 4	50 × 5	61 × 4	20 × 6

E	21 × 6	30 × 6	51 × 5	41 × 6	60 × 5	50 × 6

F	13 × 3	14 × 3	16 × 2	13 × 4	13 × 6	14 × 4

G	15 × 3	16 × 3	15 × 2	15 × 4	12 × 5	14 × 5

H	13 × 5	12 × 6	15 × 5	16 × 4	14 × 6	15 × 6

I	22 × 2	26 × 2	36 × 2	23 × 4	25 × 3	26 × 4

34 Multiply (×):

A
$$
\begin{array}{r} 23 \\ \times\ 3 \\ \hline \end{array}
\quad
\begin{array}{r} 24 \\ \times\ 3 \\ \hline \end{array}
\quad
\begin{array}{r} 26 \\ \times\ 3 \\ \hline \end{array}
\quad
\begin{array}{r} 46 \\ \times\ 2 \\ \hline \end{array}
\quad
\begin{array}{r} 25 \\ \times\ 2 \\ \hline \end{array}
\quad
\begin{array}{r} 15 \\ \times\ 4 \\ \hline \end{array}
$$

B
$$
\begin{array}{r} 35 \\ \times\ 2 \\ \hline \end{array}
\quad
\begin{array}{r} 45 \\ \times\ 2 \\ \hline \end{array}
\quad
\begin{array}{r} 35 \\ \times\ 3 \\ \hline \end{array}
\quad
\begin{array}{r} 25 \\ \times\ 4 \\ \hline \end{array}
\quad
\begin{array}{r} 22 \\ \times\ 5 \\ \hline \end{array}
\quad
\begin{array}{r} 24 \\ \times\ 5 \\ \hline \end{array}
$$

C
$$
\begin{array}{r} 32 \\ \times\ 5 \\ \hline \end{array}
\quad
\begin{array}{r} 35 \\ \times\ 4 \\ \hline \end{array}
\quad
\begin{array}{r} 34 \\ \times\ 4 \\ \hline \end{array}
\quad
\begin{array}{r} 34 \\ \times\ 5 \\ \hline \end{array}
\quad
\begin{array}{r} 44 \\ \times\ 3 \\ \hline \end{array}
\quad
\begin{array}{r} 45 \\ \times\ 3 \\ \hline \end{array}
$$

D
$$
\begin{array}{r} 45 \\ \times\ 4 \\ \hline \end{array}
\quad
\begin{array}{r} 25 \\ \times\ 5 \\ \hline \end{array}
\quad
\begin{array}{r} 55 \\ \times\ 2 \\ \hline \end{array}
\quad
\begin{array}{r} 44 \\ \times\ 4 \\ \hline \end{array}
\quad
\begin{array}{r} 56 \\ \times\ 2 \\ \hline \end{array}
\quad
\begin{array}{r} 22 \\ \times\ 6 \\ \hline \end{array}
$$

E
$$
\begin{array}{r} 32 \\ \times\ 6 \\ \hline \end{array}
\quad
\begin{array}{r} 24 \\ \times\ 6 \\ \hline \end{array}
\quad
\begin{array}{r} 25 \\ \times\ 6 \\ \hline \end{array}
\quad
\begin{array}{r} 65 \\ \times\ 2 \\ \hline \end{array}
\quad
\begin{array}{r} 33 \\ \times\ 6 \\ \hline \end{array}
\quad
\begin{array}{r} 35 \\ \times\ 5 \\ \hline \end{array}
$$

F
$$
\begin{array}{r} 46 \\ \times\ 3 \\ \hline \end{array}
\quad
\begin{array}{r} 26 \\ \times\ 6 \\ \hline \end{array}
\quad
\begin{array}{r} 36 \\ \times\ 4 \\ \hline \end{array}
\quad
\begin{array}{r} 43 \\ \times\ 5 \\ \hline \end{array}
\quad
\begin{array}{r} 54 \\ \times\ 4 \\ \hline \end{array}
\quad
\begin{array}{r} 44 \\ \times\ 5 \\ \hline \end{array}
$$

G
$$
\begin{array}{r} 34 \\ \times\ 6 \\ \hline \end{array}
\quad
\begin{array}{r} 66 \\ \times\ 2 \\ \hline \end{array}
\quad
\begin{array}{r} 55 \\ \times\ 3 \\ \hline \end{array}
\quad
\begin{array}{r} 45 \\ \times\ 5 \\ \hline \end{array}
\quad
\begin{array}{r} 56 \\ \times\ 3 \\ \hline \end{array}
\quad
\begin{array}{r} 54 \\ \times\ 5 \\ \hline \end{array}
$$

H
$$
\begin{array}{r} 56 \\ \times\ 4 \\ \hline \end{array}
\quad
\begin{array}{r} 35 \\ \times\ 6 \\ \hline \end{array}
\quad
\begin{array}{r} 42 \\ \times\ 6 \\ \hline \end{array}
\quad
\begin{array}{r} 64 \\ \times\ 3 \\ \hline \end{array}
\quad
\begin{array}{r} 65 \\ \times\ 4 \\ \hline \end{array}
\quad
\begin{array}{r} 66 \\ \times\ 4 \\ \hline \end{array}
$$

I
$$
\begin{array}{r} 43 \\ \times\ 6 \\ \hline \end{array}
\quad
\begin{array}{r} 54 \\ \times\ 6 \\ \hline \end{array}
\quad
\begin{array}{r} 66 \\ \times\ 5 \\ \hline \end{array}
\quad
\begin{array}{r} 46 \\ \times\ 6 \\ \hline \end{array}
\quad
\begin{array}{r} 56 \\ \times\ 6 \\ \hline \end{array}
\quad
\begin{array}{r} 65 \\ \times\ 6 \\ \hline \end{array}
$$

Write answers only

1 3 times 2.

2 2 times 3.

3 2 times 4.

4 3 times 3.

5 Four times three.

6 Three times four.

7 Five times two.

8 Four times four.

9 Three fives.

10 Two sixes.

11 Six twos.

12 Five threes.

13 Three sixes.

14 Four fives.

15 Five times four.

16 Six times three.

17 Multiply 4 by 3.

18 Multiply 2 by 5.

19 Multiply 5 by 4.

20 Multiply 3 by 6.

21 5 multiplied by 5.

22 6 multiplied by 4.

23 4 multiplied by 6.

24 5 multiplied by 6.

Work out on paper

25 What number is 3 times 32?

26 Multiply twenty-six by five.

27 What number is four times fifty-two?

28 What number is forty-five times four?

29 Multiply thirty-six by five.

30 What is forty-four multiplied by five?

31 What is fifty-one multiplied by six?

32 What number is six times sixty-six?

PREPARING FOR MULTIPLICATION

Work across the page

Extending addition (+):

A	21+3=	27+2=	27+4=	28+3=	27+5=
B	32+8=	25+6=	27+7=	28+5=	36+5=
C	40+7=	42+4=	45+3=	36+7=	28+8=
D	45+5=	48+3=	49+2=	42+8=	48+5=
E	49+6=	45+8=	54+3=	56+5=	48+7=
F	54+5=	56+7=	63+4=	54+8=	64+5=
G	72+4=	63+6=	64+7=	63+8=	72+8=

MULTIPLICATION TABLE: 2

Multiply (✗):

H	8×1=	9×0=	2×7=	7×2=	2×8=
I	3×7=	8×2=	3×8=	8×3=	7×3=
J	2×9=	9×2=	4×7=	7×4=	7×5=
K	8×4=	4×8=	5×7=	6×7=	7×6=
L	3×9=	9×3=	4×9=	5×8=	9×4=
M	8×5=	6×8=	8×6=	5×9=	9×5=
N	6×9=	9×6=	7×7=	8×8=	7×8=
O	8×7=	7×9=	9×7=	9×8=	9×9=

Multiply (✗):

A	38 ×2	32 ×7	29 ×3	23 ×8	67 ×3	24 ×9
B	67 ×4	85 ×4	45 ×8	68 ×3	47 ×5	56 ×7

Multiply (✖):

A	56 × 6	75 × 4	76 × 5	67 × 6	77 × 2	95 × 4
B	28 × 7	24 × 8	68 × 5	49 × 5	65 × 8	73 × 8
C	79 × 3	73 × 9	57 × 7	89 × 4	76 × 5	75 × 6
D	89 × 3	79 × 5	89 × 5	56 × 9	84 × 7	69 × 6
E	69 × 7	88 × 5	96 × 5	85 × 6	99 × 4	62 × 9
F	75 × 7	78 × 6	49 × 7	78 × 7	82 × 8	75 × 8
G	79 × 6	96 × 7	83 × 8	74 × 9	76 × 8	86 × 8
H	89 × 6	75 × 9	94 × 8	69 × 8	77 × 8	89 × 7
I	68 × 9	95 × 8	94 × 9	85 × 9	89 × 8	96 × 9

38 Multiply (×):

A	224 × 2	302 × 3	203 × 4	320 × 4	301 × 5	502 × 4
B	310 × 4	420 × 3	201 × 5	401 × 5	500 × 4	501 × 6
C	113 × 4	123 × 4	114 × 3	125 × 3	214 × 4	213 × 5
D	212 × 6	126 × 2	315 × 2	214 × 5	325 × 4	213 × 6
E	325 × 3	324 × 4	314 × 5	216 × 5	315 × 6	416 × 6
F	141 × 3	231 × 4	131 × 5	262 × 2	364 × 2	242 × 3
G	253 × 3	360 × 3	240 × 4	260 × 4	221 × 5	320 × 5
H	454 × 2	340 × 5	450 × 5	451 × 6	560 × 6	550 × 6
I	115 × 6	203 × 7	304 × 6	305 × 4	404 × 5	506 × 5

Multiply (×):

A   204 × 7   304 × 8   506 × 7   406 × 8   705 × 6   307 × 9

B   706 × 5   806 × 5   505 × 8   608 × 7   706 × 8   508 × 8

C   366 × 2   457 × 3   478 × 2   389 × 2   367 × 3   479 × 3

D   589 × 2   378 × 4   789 × 4   608 × 5   566 × 5   798 × 5

E   485 × 6   478 × 6   348 × 7   589 × 6   469 × 7   257 × 9

F   908 × 5   709 × 6   750 × 7   630 × 8   820 × 8   432 × 9

G   627 × 7   789 × 3   753 × 7   790 × 7   427 × 8   548 × 9

H   786 × 7   897 × 6   680 × 9   960 × 9   895 × 7   839 × 8

I   898 × 7   687 × 9   897 × 8   899 × 9   989 × 8   997 × 9

MULTIPLICATION WITH WORDS (2)

Write answers only

1 Eight times three.

2 Three times eight.

3 Three sevens.

4 Three nines.

5 Multiply 4 by 8.

6 Multiply 5 by 7.

7 How many is 7×6?

8 How many is 9×4?

9 How many is 8×5?

10 How many is 7×7?

11 Multiply 5×9.

12 Multiply 8 by 7.

13 9 multiplied by 6.

14 8 multiplied by 8.

15 How many is 7 times 9?

16 How many is 9 times 8?

17 8 Multiplied by 9.

18 Multiply 9 by 9.

Work these sums in your book:

19 How many is two times seventy-nine?

20 How many is three times eighty-nine?

21 What number is four times ninety-two?

22 How many is 709 multiplied by 5?

23 If three sandwiches are to be put in each lunch, how many will be needed for 58 packed lunches?

24 There are seven days in one week. How many days are there in forty-nine weeks?

25 If one metre of P. V. C. covers eight library books, how many should be covered by one hundred and five metres?

26 If there are nine balls in a box, how many will there be in one hundred and forty-four boxes?

PREPARING FOR MULTIPLICATION
Work across the page

Extending addition (+):

A	$24+ 8=$	$24+10=$	$25+ 7=$	$27+ 9=$	$28+10=$
B	$30+11=$	$32+ 9=$	$36+ 8=$	$42+ 9=$	$45+10=$
C	$48+ 9=$	$49+ 8=$	$54+11=$	$56+ 7=$	$60+11=$
D	$56+ 9=$	$63+ 7=$	$64+ 8=$	$63+ 9=$	$63+11=$
E	$72+ 8=$	$81+ 9=$	$64+10=$	$72+11=$	$96+ 4=$
F	$99+ 3=$	$90+10=$	$81+10=$	$96+ 5=$	$99+ 6-$
G	$96+ 9=$	$99+10=$	$108+ 4=$	$96+11=$	$108+ 8=$

MULTIPLICATION TABLE: 3

Multiply ($\times$):

H	$10\times2=$	$10\times3=$	$10\times0=$	$11\times2=$	$12\times2=$
I	$11\times3=$	$10\times4=$	$11\times4=$	$12\times3=$	$12\times4=$
J	$10\times5=$	$10\times6=$	$11\times5=$	$12\times5=$	$11\times6=$
K	$10\times7=$	$10\times8=$	$11\times7=$	$12\times6=$	$12\times7=$
L	$11\times8=$	$12\times8=$	$10\times9=$	$11\times9=$	$12\times9=$

Multiply ($\times$):

A	23×9	23×10	32×10	33×11	42×10	51×11
B	26×10	37×10	24×11	16×11	22×12	31×12
C	27×11	44×10	32×12	55×10	45×11	67×10
D	235×10	316×11	224×12	356×10	417×11	344×12

Multiply (✕):

A

256	416	517	403	306	508
× 11	× 12	× 10	× 11	× 12	× 10

B

406	607	515	425	788	525
× 11	× 10	× 12	× 12	× 10	× 12

C

523	989	367	725	825	467
× 11	× 10	× 12	× 12	× 12	× 12

D

678	768	638	998	742	842
× 11	× 11	× 12	× 10	× 12	× 12

E

788	908	407	505	805	675
× 11	× 11	× 12	× 12	× 12	× 12

F

954	767	867	967	975	908
× 11	× 12	× 12	× 12	× 12	× 12

G

693	599	639	693	895	696
× 11	× 11	× 12	× 12	× 11	× 12

H

799	588	689	609	709	584
× 11	× 12	× 12	× 12	× 12	× 12

I

999	875	884	909	984	899
× 11	× 12	× 12	× 10	× 12	× 12

Write answers only

1 Multiply seven by two.

2 Find the product of 10×6.

3 Find the product of 9×10.

4 Twelve threes.

5 Nine multiplied by nine.

6 Find the product of 12×9.

Work out on paper

7 Multiply seventy-eight by five.

8 What number is seven times five-hundred-and-thirty-two?

9 What number is equal to eight times four-hundred-and-twenty-seven?

10 Find the product of eleven and two-hundred-and nine.

11 Find the product of nine and four-hundred-and-eighteen.

12 What is the product of three-hundred-and-sixty-six and eleven?

13 What equals nine times six-hundred-and-thirty-five?

14 Find the product of twelve and three-hundred-and-eighty-four.

15 If a machine can stamp 580 letters in one hour, how many will it stamp in 9 hours?

16 If a ship is to average 809 kilometres per day, how far will it cruise in 12 days?

✕ ✕ ✕ **CHECK YOUR LONG MULTIPLICATION** ✕ ✕ ✕

✕

				Further Practice
				Page
A	314 × 10	560 × 20	405 × 60	45 rows A & B
B	423 × 21	419 × 22	509 × 23	45 rows C–F
C	207 × 24	360 × 31	580 × 24	46 rows A–C
D	252 × 15	406 × 35	505 × 36	46 rows D–F
E	806 × 45	655 × 38	859 × 47	47 rows A–C
F	450 × 18	780 × 65	4080 × 85	47 rows D–F

Multiply (×):

A
$$\begin{array}{r} 231 \\ \times\ 10 \\ \hline \end{array}$$
$$\begin{array}{r} 204 \\ \times\ 10 \\ \hline \end{array}$$
$$\begin{array}{r} 560 \\ \times\ 10 \\ \hline \end{array}$$
$$\begin{array}{r} 780 \\ \times\ 10 \\ \hline \end{array}$$

B
$$\begin{array}{r} 426 \\ \times\ 20 \\ \hline \end{array}$$
$$\begin{array}{r} 420 \\ \times\ 50 \\ \hline \end{array}$$
$$\begin{array}{r} 605 \\ \times\ 60 \\ \hline \end{array}$$
$$\begin{array}{r} 505 \\ \times\ 80 \\ \hline \end{array}$$

C
$$\begin{array}{r} 234 \\ \times\ 21 \\ \hline \end{array}$$
$$\begin{array}{r} 174 \\ \times\ 21 \\ \hline \end{array}$$
$$\begin{array}{r} 178 \\ \times\ 21 \\ \hline \end{array}$$
$$\begin{array}{r} 216 \\ \times\ 31 \\ \hline \end{array}$$

D
$$\begin{array}{r} 247 \\ \times\ 31 \\ \hline \end{array}$$
$$\begin{array}{r} 388 \\ \times\ 22 \\ \hline \end{array}$$
$$\begin{array}{r} 519 \\ \times\ 22 \\ \hline \end{array}$$
$$\begin{array}{r} 456 \\ \times\ 23 \\ \hline \end{array}$$

E
$$\begin{array}{r} 179 \\ \times\ 31 \\ \hline \end{array}$$
$$\begin{array}{r} 207 \\ \times\ 23 \\ \hline \end{array}$$
$$\begin{array}{r} 208 \\ \times\ 32 \\ \hline \end{array}$$
$$\begin{array}{r} 409 \\ \times\ 22 \\ \hline \end{array}$$

F
$$\begin{array}{r} 608 \\ \times\ 23 \\ \hline \end{array}$$
$$\begin{array}{r} 709 \\ \times\ 32 \\ \hline \end{array}$$
$$\begin{array}{r} 507 \\ \times\ 23 \\ \hline \end{array}$$
$$\begin{array}{r} 706 \\ \times\ 33 \\ \hline \end{array}$$

46 Multiply (×):

A

$$\begin{array}{r} 340 \\ \times\ 21 \end{array}$$

(1)
340
6800
7140

$$\begin{array}{r} 260 \\ \times\ 21 \end{array}$$

$$\begin{array}{r} 380 \\ \times\ 22 \end{array}$$

(2)
760
7600
8360

$$\begin{array}{r} 470 \\ \times\ 31 \end{array}$$

B

$$\begin{array}{r} 470 \\ \times\ 23 \end{array}$$

$$\begin{array}{r} 580 \\ \times\ 31 \end{array}$$

$$\begin{array}{r} 607 \\ \times\ 24 \end{array}$$

(3)
2428
12140
14568

$$\begin{array}{r} 705 \\ \times\ 32 \end{array}$$

C

$$\begin{array}{r} 731 \\ \times\ 25 \end{array}$$

(4)
$$\begin{array}{r} 453 \\ \times\ 25 \end{array}$$
2265
9060
11325

(5)
$$\begin{array}{r} 678 \\ \times\ 32 \end{array}$$
13256
20340
21696

(6)
$$\begin{array}{r} 596 \\ \times\ 41 \end{array}$$
596
23840
24436

D

$$\begin{array}{r} 709 \\ \times\ 15 \end{array}$$

$$\begin{array}{r} 342 \\ \times\ 15 \end{array}$$

$$\begin{array}{r} 516 \\ \times\ 25 \end{array}$$

$$\begin{array}{r} 347 \\ \times\ 17 \end{array}$$

E

(7)
$$\begin{array}{r} 408 \\ \times\ 35 \end{array}$$
2040
12240
14280

$$\begin{array}{r} 305 \\ \times\ 26 \end{array}$$

$$\begin{array}{r} 505 \\ \times\ 18 \end{array}$$

$$\begin{array}{r} 608 \\ \times\ 35 \end{array}$$

F

(8)
$$\begin{array}{r} 668 \\ \times\ 25 \end{array}$$
3340
13360
16700

(9)
$$\begin{array}{r} 546 \\ \times\ 35 \end{array}$$
2730
16380
19110

(10)
$$\begin{array}{r} 505 \\ \times\ 44 \end{array}$$
2020
20200
22220

$$\begin{array}{r} 705 \\ \times\ 46 \end{array}$$

Multiply (✗):

A

709	⑪ 806	⑫ 690	⑬ 780
× 17	× 35	× 243	× 152
	4030	23070	1560
	24180	27600	39000
	28210	29670	405160

B

⑭ 725	⑮ 808	655	⑯ 578
× 42	× 45	× 28	× 355
1450	4040		2890
29000	32320		28900
30450	36360		31790

C

589	789	825	⑰ 907
× 38	× 47	× 46	× 54
			3628
			45350
			48978

D

650	550	750	850
× 16	× 36	× 38	× 48

E

⑱ 460	⑲ 680	⑳ 6040	8020
× 45	× 455	× 25	× 65
2300	3400	30200	
18400	34000	120800	
20700	37400	151000	

F

1204	2015	3050	5060
× 160	× 236	× 206	× 402

÷

CHECK YOUR **DIVISION**

					Further Practice	
					Table	Pages
A	2)2 4	3)3 6 9	4)8 0 4	3)9 6 0	1	50
B	5)1 5	3)1 2 9	4)2 0 4	6)3 0 0	1	51
C	3)6 3 4	4)2 0 5	5)2 0 1	6)3 6 5	1	52
D	2)5 2	4)8 5 2	3)7 2 3	6)9 0 6	1	53
E	4)1 9 0	5)7 0 1	6)9 0 0	6)3 8 7	1	54 to 56
F	3)5 0 4	5)6 4 0	7)8 0 5	8)9 9 6	2	58
G	2)1 7 9	4)3 7 9	6)5 3 0	7)3 3 4	2	59 & 60
H	7)5 8 9	8)6 0 0	5)3 9 0 1	9)8 0 5 2	2	61 & 62
I	9)6 5 7 2	12)5 7 0 0	11)6 5 0 2	12)1 1 6 0	3	65

PREPARING FOR DIVISION
Work across the page

Take away (—):

A	$13-12=$	$14-12=$	$16-15=$	$17-15=$	$17-16=$
B	$19-18=$	$15-12=$	$17-12=$	$18-15=$	$18-16=$
C	$19-16=$	$21-18=$	$23-18=$	$24-20=$	$25-24=$
D	$27-24=$	$29-24=$	$33-30=$	$37-36=$	$38-36=$
E	$26-25=$	$29-25=$	$19-15=$	$35-30=$	$39-36=$

Complete these sums

Multiply (✕):

F	$2\times\ =4$	$3\times\ =6$	$3\times\ =9$	$2\times\ =8$
G	$\times 2=10$	$3\times\ =12$	$2\times\ =12$	$\times 4=8$
H	$4\times\ =12$	$\times 3=15$	$3\times\ =18$	$4\times\ =16$
I	$\times 4=20$	$6\times\ =12$	$5\times\ =20$	$6\times\ =18$
J	$5\times\ =25$	$\times 6=24$	$5\times\ =30$	$6\times\ =30$
K	$4\times\ =24$	$\times 5=30$	$\times 6=30$	$\times 6=36$

DIVISION TABLE: 1
Write answers only

Divide (÷):

A	$5\div 2=$	$7\div 2=$	$7\div 3=$	$8\div 3=$	$9\div 2=$
B	$10\div 3=$	$11\div 2=$	$11\div 4=$	$12\div 4=$	$13\div 3=$
C	$13\div 2=$	$13\div 4=$	$14\div 4=$	$11\div 5=$	$13\div 5=$
D	$16\div 4=$	$17\div 4=$	$19\div 4=$	$20\div 4=$	$21\div 4=$
E	$15\div 5=$	$16\div 5=$	$18\div 3=$	$19\div 3=$	$20\div 3=$
F	$22\div 4=$	$24\div 4=$	$26\div 4=$	$17\div 5=$	$19\div 5=$
G	$21\div 5=$	$23\div 5=$	$26\div 5=$	$28\div 5=$	$29\div 5=$
H	$23\div 4=$	$30\div 5=$	$32\div 5=$	$14\div 6=$	$19\div 6=$
I	$34\div 5=$	$22\div 6=$	$27\div 6=$	$33\div 6=$	$39\div 6=$

50 Divide (÷):

A   2)24   3)36   2)46   3)63   4)44

B   2)66   3)66   4)48   2)68   2)84

C   3)93   4)84   3)69   4)88   3)99

D   3)333   2)224   3)363   2)426   2)284

E   3)366   2)642   3)663   2)648   3)393

F   4)488   3)696   4)848   3)996   4)884

G   2)202   3)306   2)604   4)408   3)609

H   2)806   3)909   4)808   4)480   2)680

I   3)660   2)860   3)960   4)840   3)990

J   4)880   3)600   2)800   3)900   4)800

Divide (÷):

A $2)\overline{1\ 2}$ $4)\overline{1\ 2}$ $3)\overline{1\ 5}$ $5)\overline{1\ 5}$ $4)\overline{1\ 6}$

B $6)\overline{1\ 8}$ $3)\overline{1\ 8}$ $4)\overline{2\ 4}$ $5)\overline{2\ 5}$ $6)\overline{2\ 4}$

C $4)\overline{2\ 0}$ $5)\overline{2\ 0}$ $5)\overline{3\ 0}$ $6)\overline{3\ 0}$ $6)\overline{3\ 6}$

D $2)\overline{1\ 2\ 2}$ $2)\overline{1\ 2\ 6}$ $3)\overline{1\ 2\ 6}$ $6)\overline{1\ 2\ 6}$ $3)\overline{1\ 5\ 6}$

E $4)\overline{1\ 2\ 8}$ $5)\overline{1\ 5\ 5}$ $4)\overline{1\ 6\ 8}$ $3)\overline{1\ 8\ 3}$ $2)\overline{1\ 0\ 4}$

F $5)\overline{1\ 0\ 5}$ $4)\overline{2\ 0\ 8}$ $5)\overline{2\ 0\ 5}$ $6)\overline{1\ 8\ 6}$ $4)\overline{2\ 4\ 8}$

G $5)\overline{2\ 5\ 5}$ $6)\overline{2\ 4\ 6}$ $5)\overline{3\ 0\ 5}$ $6)\overline{3\ 0\ 6}$ $6)\overline{3\ 6\ 6}$

H $2)\overline{8\ 0}$ $3)\overline{9\ 0}$ $2)\overline{1\ 2\ 0}$ $3)\overline{1\ 5\ 0}$ $4)\overline{1\ 6\ 0}$

I $5)\overline{1\ 5\ 0}$ $4)\overline{2\ 4\ 0}$ $5)\overline{2\ 5\ 0}$ $6)\overline{1\ 8\ 0}$ $6)\overline{2\ 4\ 0}$

J $4)\overline{2\ 0\ 0}$ $5)\overline{2\ 0\ 0}$ $5)\overline{3\ 0\ 0}$ $6)\overline{3\ 0\ 0}$ $6)\overline{3\ 6\ 0}$

52   Divide (÷):

A   2)4 4 3   2)6 4 5   3)6 3 5   3)6 6 8   4)1 2 5

B   5)1 0 6   5)1 0 7   4)1 6 9   3)1 5 7   3)1 8 8

C   4)2 0 5   4)2 0 7   5)1 5 7   6)1 2 9   4)2 0 9

D   5)1 5 8   4)2 4 7   5)2 0 7   6)1 8 9   4)2 4 9

E   5)2 0 9   5)2 5 8   5)2 5 9   6)2 4 9   5)3 0 7

F   6)3 0 7   5)3 0 9   6)3 0 9   6)3 6 8   6)3 6 9

G   2)1 2 1   3)1 2 1   3)1 5 2   3)1 8 2   4)1 2 3

H   4)1 6 1   5)1 0 2   5)1 0 4   4)2 0 3   5)1 5 3

I   5)2 0 1   6)1 8 5   6)2 4 4   5)2 5 4   5)3 0 1

J   6)3 0 3   4)2 4 3   6)3 0 5   5)3 0 4   6)3 6 5

Divide (÷):

A   2)3 2   3)4 2   2)7 2   3)7 2   3)7 5

B   2)9 2   3)4 8   3)7 8   4)3 2   4)9 2

C   5)6 5   6)7 2   4)5 6   4)9 6   5)7 5

D   2)5 0   2)7 0   2)9 0   4)6 0   5)6 0

E   4)6 4   5)8 0   6)7 8   6)8 4   6)9 0

F   2)4 3 2   3)3 4 2   3)6 4 5   4)8 5 2   3)9 7 8

G   5)5 6 5   5)5 7 5   6)6 7 8   4)8 6 4   6)6 8 4

H   5)5 6 0   4)8 6 0   5)5 8 0   6)6 9 0   6)6 9 6

I   2)3 2 4   3)7 2 3   3)7 8 9   4)9 6 8   5)6 5 5

J   6)7 2 6   5)7 5 5   6)7 8 6   6)8 4 6   6)9 6 6

54   Divide (÷):

A   2)5 2 6   3)7 5 6   5)5 7 0   4)9 2 8   4)6 4 8

B   2)3 0 4   2)5 0 6   2)7 0 8   4)6 0 4   2)9 0 8

C   5)6 0 5   4)6 0 8   5)7 0 5   5)8 0 5   6)9 0 6

D   3)4 0 2   3)4 0 5   4)5 0 4   4)5 0 0   4)5 8 0

E   2)1 1 0   4)1 8 0   5)1 7 0   6)1 5 0   6)2 1 0

F   5)6 0 6   4)6 0 6   3)2 0 0   3)7 0 0   4)6 0 3

G   3)9 0 0   4)8 0 0   4)6 0 0   5)7 0 0   6)9 0 0

H   4)2 0 2   5)1 5 0   6)1 8 0   5)6 0 3   6)3 0 5

I   4)9 0 0   5)7 0 4   5)5 0 4   6)1 9 0   6)2 0 7

J   6)2 7 0   6)7 8 1   5)3 0 2   6)9 0 5   6)8 7 0

Write answers only

1 How many threes make twelve?

2 How many fours make sixteen?

3 Share eighteen cakes among three people.

4 Share twenty marbles among four boys.

5 How many fours make twenty-four?

6 Share twenty-five sweets among five children.

7 Divide twenty-three by five.

8 Divide twenty-seven by four.

9 Share twenty-four marbles among six boys.

10 How many sixes make thirty?

Work out on paper

11 Divide 210 children into five classes.

12 How many fives in three-hundred-and-three?

13 Share three-hundred-and-six children equally among six 'buses.

14 A man is to plant 820 cabbages in five rows. How many plants will be in each row?

15 Divide two-hundred-and-seventy into six equal groups.

16 Share three-hundred-and thirty-six bottles of milk equally among six classes.

56 Divide (÷):

A   3)198   3)199   3)912   5)252   6)204

B   5)180   5)212   4)182   3)500   6)150

C   4)602   5)703   5)801   6)740   6)790

D   5)502   4)900   4)803   6)799   6)804

E   4)641   5)752   5)759   6)810   5)803

F   5)182   6)200   6)210   5)225   6)262

G   4)223   5)234   6)272   6)218   6)279

H   4)260   6)303   6)320   6)323   5)278

I   5)279   6)339   5)334   5)280   6)390

J   4)267   5)309   6)379   6)389   6)399

PREPARING FOR DIVISION
Work across the page

Take away (—):

A	$26-21=$	$30-28=$	$32-27=$	$39-35=$	$41-35=$
B	$52-45=$	$53-48=$	$51-49=$	$60-54=$	$62-56=$
C	$70-63=$	$71-64=$	$78-72=$	$71-63=$	$89-81=$

Complete these sums:

Multiply (✗):

D	$2\times\ =14$	$7\times\ =21$	$8\times\ =16$	$\times7\ =21$
E	$\times4\ =28$	$\times3\ =24$	$\times9\ =18$	$9\times\ =18$
F	$9\times\ =27$	$5\times\ =35$	$\times7\ =35$	$\times8\ =32$
G	$\times9\ =36$	$4\times\ =36$	$8\times\ =40$	$7\times\ =42$
H	$5\times\ =40$	$\times7\ =42$	$\times7\ =49$	$6\times\ =48$
I	$\times8\ =48$	$\times8\ =64$	$\times6\ =54$	$6\times\ =54$
J	$9\times\ =54$	$8\times\ =56$	$7\times\ =56$	$9\times\ =63$
K	$9\times\ =72$	$8\times\ =72$	$9\times\ =63$	$\times9\ =81$

DIVISION TABLE: 2
Write answers only

Divide (÷):

A	$14\div2=$	$16\div2=$	$21\div3=$	$17\div8=$	$18\div7=$
B	$19\div2=$	$20\div7=$	$29\div4=$	$28\div7=$	$33\div7=$
C	$23\div9=$	$22\div8=$	$30\div9=$	$33\div4=$	$27\div8=$
D	$36\div4=$	$37\div7=$	$39\div4=$	$38\div5=$	$40\div6=$
E	$37\div9=$	$41\div5=$	$41\div7=$	$43\div6=$	$41\div8=$
F	$47\div5=$	$46\div8=$	$47\div6=$	$42\div9=$	$44\div7=$
G	$50\div6=$	$50\div7=$	$53\div8=$	$48\div9=$	$58\div8=$
H	$59\div7=$	$56\div6=$	$55\div9=$	$65\div8=$	$62\div9=$
I	$66\div7=$	$73\div8=$	$70\div9=$	$79\div8=$	$80\div9=$

58

Divide (÷):

A   2)6 8 0   3)6 0 0   2)5 0 8   3)5 0 1   2)5 4 2

B   3)5 0 7   3)8 0 0   4)7 0 4   4)7 0 8   5)7 3 0

C   4)9 0 9   6)8 8 0   5)7 4 0   5)8 6 0   4)7 4 0

D   4)7 8 0   5)8 9 0   6)8 9 0   7)8 0 0   6)9 0 9

E   5)9 4 0   6)9 5 0   7)8 8 0   7)9 6 8   7)9 2 0

F   7)8 9 0   8)9 7 0   7)9 3 0   7)9 4 0   8)9 0 4

G   7)9 5 0   7)9 6 0   8)9 8 7   9)9 9 9   7)9 0 0

H   8)8 9 0   7)9 0 3   6)9 8 0   7)9 0 7   5)9 4 5

I   5)9 4 9   6)9 5 4   8)9 9 0   6)9 5 9   7)9 2 9

J   4)7 9 0   7)8 0 9   7)9 7 0   8)9 9 9   7)9 7 9

Divide (÷):

A   2)147   3)189   2)154   3)201   2)176

B   2)198   3)204   2)199   3)219   4)192

C   3)229   4)228   3)231   3)237   4)232

D   3)249   3)265   5)260   4)268   4)270

E   4)300   3)280   3)290   4)310   5)309

F   3)298   4)312   4)316   5)335   4)330

G   4)349   4)353   5)357   5)386   4)356

H   5)390   4)389   4)390   6)398   4)394

I   5)392   6)401   5)395   4)397   6)402

J   4)380   5)419   7)149   6)410   7)161

60 Divide (÷):

A   5)4 2 9   5)4 4 6   6)4 0 7   6)4 5 0   7)1 5 0

B   5)4 8 0   6)4 1 0   6)4 1 4   5)4 9 0   7)1 7 1

C   6)4 2 9   6)4 5 8   5)4 9 7   7)1 6 8   7)1 7 5

D   6)4 6 8   7)2 1 8   6)4 5 9   6)4 7 0   7)2 2 9

E   6)4 7 3   7)2 3 6   7)2 4 0   6)4 7 8   6)5 0 9

F   7)2 3 7   6)5 2 7   7)2 4 4   6)5 3 7   7)2 5 0

G   6)5 9 6   7)2 6 0   8)1 6 9   7)2 6 6   7)3 0 6

H   7)3 1 7   8)1 0 4   7)3 3 3   8)1 7 8   8)1 8 0

I   8)1 8 4   9)1 0 8   9)1 1 7   8)2 0 0   9)1 8 9

J   8)1 9 0   7)3 2 0   7)3 3 9   9)2 1 6   8)2 1 5

Divide (÷):

A 7)3 4 0   7)4 0 0   8)2 4 0   7)4 0 6   9)2 7 0

B 8)3 3 0   8)4 0 6   7)4 1 0   7)4 2 0   9)2 0 5

C 8)2 6 1   9)2 2 0   9)2 2 2   8)2 6 8   8)2 7 0

D 7)4 2 6   7)4 5 8   8)3 2 0   8)3 0 0   7)4 6 9

E 7)5 6 0   9)4 5 0   8)3 0 5   7)5 3 5   7)6 3 0

F 8)4 0 0   8)3 7 0   7)5 8 9   9)4 9 0   7)6 0 8

G 8)4 7 0   9)5 0 4   9)6 0 8   8)5 1 0   7)4 9 2

H 9)9 4 0   9)6 3 3   8)8 8 0   9)9 5 0   8)7 2 0

I 9)7 2 0   9)9 5 5   8)8 0 6   9)8 1 0   9)7 6 9

J 7)7 6 3   8)8 5 6   9)9 6 0   8)8 0 7   9)9 8 0

62   **Divide (÷):**

A   4)8 4 4 8   5)1 0 0 0   5)3 5 0 0   4)1 0 8 0   4)3 0 7 8

B   5)3 9 4 0   6)4 0 7 0   7)3 0 6 7   6)5 4 5 4   7)4 2 4 9

C   7)3 5 6 3   8)3 2 4 8   6)5 8 8 0   8)3 8 8 0   9)3 6 5 4

D   6)4 7 9 9   7)4 8 3 3   8)3 8 5 1   9)4 5 6 0   9)5 0 1 1

E   7)5 0 3 7   8)4 8 7 2   8)5 3 8 0   9)5 1 0 0   8)5 3 9 7

F   9)5 1 2 0   9)6 0 0 0   8)5 4 0 0   8)5 9 5 2   9)5 2 2 0

G   8)6 0 8 0   9)5 3 1 0   7)5 3 8 9   9)6 0 3 0   8)6 4 7 2

H   8)7 0 4 0   7)6 0 7 5   8)7 2 3 2   9)7 2 5 4   9)8 1 0 0

I   9)8 1 0 1   8)7 2 1 0   9)8 1 5 3   8)8 0 9 0   9)8 1 9 0

J   7)7 0 1 4   9)9 6 3 0   8)8 0 6 4   9)8 0 1 0   9)9 0 7 9

Write answers only

1 How many threes in twenty-one?

2 How many threes equal twenty-seven?

3 Divide thirty by four.

4 Share forty-five equally into five parts.

5 How many sixes are contained in 48?

6 How many times can 7 be taken from 28?

7 How many times can 8 be taken from 32?

8 Divide 42 sweets equally amongst 6 girls.

9 Share fifty-six into seven equal parts.

10 How many nines make thirty-six?

11 Divide fifty-four into nine equal parts.

12 How many nines are equal to sixty-three?

13 $\frac{1}{2}$ of 12.

14 $\frac{1}{2}$ of 16.

15 $\frac{1}{3}$ of 15.

16 $\frac{1}{3}$ of 18.

17 $\frac{1}{4}$ of 20.

18 $\frac{1}{4}$ of 24.

19 $\frac{1}{3}$ of 21.

20 $\frac{1}{3}$ of 27.

21 $\frac{1}{5}$ of 25.

22 $\frac{1}{5}$ of 40.

23 $\frac{1}{4}$ of 28.

24 $\frac{1}{4}$ of 32.

25 Find one-half of eighteen.

26 What is one-third of twenty-four?

27 Make twenty-one less by one-third.

28 Reduce twenty-seven by one-third.

PREPARING FOR DIVISION
Work across the page

Write answers only:

Take away (−):

A	$23-20=$	$37-30=$	$30-22=$	$33-24=$	$46-36=$
B	$52-44=$	$55-48=$	$70-60=$	$73-66=$	$80-72=$
C	$85-77=$	$93-84=$	$101-99=$	$102-96=$	$111-108=$

Multiply (×): Complete these sums:

D	$2\times \quad =20$	$11\times \quad = 22$	$\times 12 = 24$	$\times 11 = 33$
E	$11\times \quad =44$	$12\times \quad = 36$	$\times 12 = 48$	$12\times \quad = 60$
F	$\times 5 =60$	$\times 11 = 66$	$11\times \quad = 77$	$\times 12 = 72$
G	$6\times \quad =72$	$12\times \quad = 84$	$\times 7 = 84$	$8\times \quad = 80$
H	$11\times \quad =88$	$8\times \quad = 96$	$12\times \quad = 96$	$\times 11 = 99$
I	$\times 9 =90$	$12\times \quad =108$	$\times 12 =108$	$9\times \quad =108$

DIVISION TABLE: 3
Write answers only:

Divide (÷):

A	$21\div 10=$	$23\div 11=$	$31\div 11=$	$37\div 10=$	$34\div 11=$
B	$19\div 12=$	$22\div 12=$	$25\div 12=$	$30\div 12=$	$34\div 12=$
C	$36\div 12=$	$41\div 10=$	$38\div 12=$	$47\div 11=$	$41\div 12=$
D	$47\div 12=$	$51\div 12=$	$56\div 10=$	$57\div 12=$	$60\div 12=$
E	$62\div 11=$	$62\div 12=$	$70\div 12=$	$73\div 12=$	$70\div 11=$
F	$80\div 12=$	$83\div 12=$	$85\div 10=$	$87\div 12=$	$90\div 12=$
G	$90\div 11=$	$93\div 12=$	$95\div 8=$	$96\div 12=$	$98\div 11=$
H	$99\div 12=$	$100\div 12=$	$99\div 10=$	$100\div 9=$	$102\div 12=$
I	$105\div 12=$	$110\div 12=$	$101\div 11=$	$112\div 12=$	$118\div 12=$

Divide (÷):

A   7)8 9 0 0   8)8 7 2 1   9)9 8 4 7   8)6 4 7 2   9)7 7 3 8

B   9)8 0 0 5   10)1 0 0 0   11)1 1 0 0   10)9 5 0 3   11)4 6 0 0

C   12)2 4 3 6   12)1 6 0 9   9)1 0 8 0   12)1 8 0 1   12)1 9 5 0

D   11)4 7 0 8   10)8 0 6 1   12)3 0 5 0   12)3 3 3 3   11)6 0 0 6

E   10)9 7 0 0   12)4 3 6 9   12)4 5 0 0   11)3 9 9 0   12)5 4 0 1

F   10)9 0 8 2   11)4 3 1 2   12)2 2 1 0   12)2 2 8 1   12)3 4 2 0

G   12)4 7 1 6   12)8 2 3 3   11)7 6 2 8   11)6 4 6 0   12)8 3 3 0

H   9)8 1 0 1   12)8 3 4 0   12)9 4 0 3   10)9 0 0 1   12)1 0 0 8

I   12)1 0 4 0   12)1 1 0 7   11)1 0 9 0   12)1 1 5 7   12)1 1 7 0

J   11)2 0 0 0   12)1 3 0 0   12)1 2 0 2   11)1 1 0 1   12)1 1 9 9

FRACTIONS
Write answers only

1   $\frac{1}{2}$ of 10.

2   $\frac{1}{2}$ of 16.

3   $\frac{1}{3}$ of 12.

4   $\frac{1}{4}$ of 12.

5   $\frac{1}{3}$ of 15.

6   $\frac{1}{4}$ of 16.

7   $\frac{1}{2}$ of 18.

8   $\frac{1}{3}$ of 18.

9   $\frac{1}{3}$ of 21.

10   $\frac{1}{4}$ of 20.

11   $\frac{1}{4}$ of 24.

12   $\frac{1}{4}$ of 32.

13   $\frac{1}{4}$ of 28.

14   $\frac{1}{3}$ of 24.

15   $\frac{1}{3}$ of 30.

16   $\frac{1}{3}$ of 27.

17   $\frac{1}{5}$ of 10.

18   $\frac{1}{5}$ of 15.

19   $\frac{1}{5}$ of 25.

20   $\frac{1}{6}$ of 12.

21   $\frac{1}{8}$ of 16.

22   $\frac{1}{6}$ of 18.

23   $\frac{1}{8}$ of 24.

24   $\frac{1}{6}$ of 30.

25   $\frac{1}{8}$ of 32.

26   $\frac{1}{9}$ of 18.

27   $\frac{1}{6}$ of 42.

28   $\frac{1}{7}$ of 21.

29   $\frac{1}{7}$ of 35.

30   $\frac{1}{7}$ of 28.

31   $\frac{1}{5}$ of 35.

32   $\frac{1}{7}$ of 42.

33   $\frac{1}{7}$ of 56.

34   $\frac{1}{6}$ of 54.

35   $\frac{1}{8}$ of 56.

36   $\frac{1}{7}$ of 63.

37   $\frac{1}{3}$ of 9.

38   $\frac{2}{3}$ of 9.

39   $\frac{1}{5}$ of 20.

40   $\frac{2}{5}$ of 20.

41   $\frac{3}{4}$ of 20.

42   $\frac{4}{5}$ of 20.

43   $\frac{1}{7}$ of 14.

44   $\frac{2}{7}$ of 21.

45   $\frac{3}{7}$ of 28.

46   $\frac{1}{8}$ of 24.

47   $\frac{3}{8}$ of 40.

48   $\frac{5}{8}$ of 48.

49   $\frac{1}{9}$ of 27.

50   $\frac{2}{9}$ of 36.

51   $\frac{7}{9}$ of 45.

52   $\frac{2}{7}$ of 63.

53   $\frac{5}{6}$ of 42.

54   $\frac{1}{10}$ of 50.

55   $\frac{4}{9}$ of 54.

56   $\frac{1}{12}$ of 60.

57   $\frac{5}{12}$ of 72.

58   $\frac{6}{7}$ of 56.

59   $\frac{5}{9}$ of 63.

60   $\frac{7}{12}$ of 84.

				Further Practice
				Page
A	20)4 0	31)6 2	42)8 4	68 rows A–C
B	21)4 3	32)6 6	22)6 9	68 rows D–G
C	60)1 2 0	30)1 5 0	40)1 6 0	68 rows H & I
D	21)2 3 1	31)3 7 2	22)6 8 2	69 rows A–C
E	30)3 6 3 0	40)8 0 0 0	32)6 5 2 8	69 rows D–F
F	31)1 2 7 1	19)2 2 9 9	74)3 0 1 1 8	70 rows A–E

68   Divide (÷):

A   10)‾5‾0   20)‾4‾0   20)‾6‾0   30)‾6‾0   40)‾8‾0

B   11)‾2‾2   21)‾2‾1   21)‾4‾2   21)‾6‾3   22)‾4‾4

C   31)‾6‾2   22)‾6‾6   32)‾6‾4   33)‾6‾6   33)‾9‾9

D   20)‾2‾1   20)‾4‾1   21)‾2‾2   21)‾4‾3   30)‾6‾1

E   22)‾4‾5   21)‾2‾4   21)‾4‾4   31)‾3‾4   31)‾6‾3

F   30)‾6‾2   21)‾6‾5   22)‾4‾6   30)‾9‾3   22)‾6‾8

G   23)‾4‾7   22)‾6‾9   21)‾8‾6   22)‾8‾9   31)‾9‾6

H   50)‾1‾0‾0   20)‾1‾0‾0   60)‾1‾2‾0   30)‾1‾2‾0   40)‾1‾2‾0

I   20)‾1‾2‾0   50)‾1‾5‾0   30)‾1‾5‾0   40)‾1‾6‾0   20)‾1‾4‾0

Divide (÷):

A   20)$\overline{4\ 2\ 0}$ 21)$\overline{2\ 3\ 1}$ 21)$\overline{4\ 4\ 1}$ 31)$\overline{3\ 4\ 1}$

B   30)$\overline{6\ 3\ 0}$ 31)$\overline{6\ 5\ 1}$ 41)$\overline{4\ 5\ 1}$ 41)$\overline{8\ 6\ 1}$

C   22)$\overline{2\ 4\ 2}$ 21)$\overline{4\ 6\ 2}$ 22)$\overline{4\ 8\ 4}$ 21)$\overline{6\ 9\ 3}$

D   20)$\overline{2\ 4\ 2\ 0}$ 30)$\overline{6\ 9\ 3\ 0}$ 21)$\overline{4\ 6\ 6\ 2}$ 32)$\overline{3\ 8\ 7\ 2}$

E   20)$\overline{4\ 0\ 0}$ 40)$\overline{8\ 0\ 0}$ 30)$\overline{9\ 0\ 0\ 0}$ 21)$\overline{2\ 2\ 2\ 6}$

F   31)$\overline{3\ 2\ 2\ 4}$ 22)$\overline{2\ 8\ 6\ 0}$ 30)$\overline{6\ 0\ 9\ 0}$ 31)$\overline{6\ 2\ 9\ 3}$

70 Divide (÷):

A   21)6 4 2 6   23)4 8 5 3   24)5 0 6 4   41)4 2 2 5

B   31)1 5 8 1   32)1 2 8 0   31)1 2 4 1   23)1 6 2 0

C   22)1 2 0 0   44)1 3 8 1   35)1 0 7 3   55)1 2 0 9

D   43)5 1 7 0   19)2 0 9 3   29)3 8 1 4   18)4 0 0 1

E   39)9 0 0 1   54)1 6 6 8 7   73)3 0 9 0 4   84)4 0 0 7 6